Stone
the Crow

John Galloway

Series consultants:
Cliff Moon and Lorraine Petersen

nasen
NASEN House, 4/5 Amber Business Village, Amber Close,
Amington, Tamworth, Staffordshire B77 4RP

Rising Stars UK Ltd.
22 Grafton Street, London W1S 4EX
www.risingstars-uk.com

The right of John Galloway to be identified as the author of
this work has been asserted by him in accordance with the
Copyright, Design and Patents Act 1988.

Published 2007

Text, design and layout © Rising Stars UK Ltd.
Cover design: Button plc
Illustrator: Shoo Rayner
Text design and typesetting: Andy Wilson
Publisher: Gill Budgell
Commissioning editor: Catherine Baker
Editor: Clare Robertson
Series consultants: Cliff Moon and Lorraine Petersen

All rights reserved. No part of this publication may be reproduced,
stored in a retrieval system, or transmitted in any form by any means,
electronic, mechanical, photocopying, recording or otherwise without
the prior permission of Rising Stars UK Ltd.

British Library Cataloguing in Publication Data.
A CIP record for this book is available from the British Library

ISBN: 978-1-84680-314-7

Printed by Craft Print International Limited, Singapore

Contents

Characters

Hal   He's sporty and he likes to show off. He sometimes acts without thinking.

Naz   He is Hal's best friend. He sticks with Hal, even when he gets them into trouble.

Tree Spirit   A very wise spirit, as old as the wood itself. It always talks quietly.

Boggart A playful spirit that can change shape.

Crow A magical talking crow.

Narrator The narrator tells the story.

Scene 1
Target practice

Narrator   Hal and Naz are walking home
from school. They are taking
the short cut through Wizard's Wood,
even though people say odd things
happen there.

Naz   What was that?

Hal   Nothing.

Naz   It sounded like a whisper.
Someone saying, "Turn back.
Don't walk this way."

Hal   Don't be silly.

Tree Spirit (*quietly*) Go back. Take the long way.

Naz   Did you hear it?

Tree Spirit You'll be sorry.
Odd things happen in these woods.

Naz   Okay, now I'm scared.

Hal   Don't be such a wuss.
It's just the wind in the trees.

Naz   Maybe weird things *do* happen
in these woods. What if something
comes after us?

Hal   Then I'll just do this.

Narrator Hal picks up a stone from the ground
and throws it at a tree. He misses.

Naz   You missed.

Hal   I'll show you.

Narrator Hal picks up another stone
and this time he hits a big oak tree.

Tree Spirit Ouch!

Naz   What was that?

Hal   Nothing. You're hearing things.

Naz   Okay, so you can hit a tree.
But what about something that moves?

Hal   I can hit a moving target.
See that crow?

Narrator A big, black crow is flying
around the tops of the trees.
Hal throws a stone at it but he misses.

Crow   Oi! Rotten kids. They come into
our nice quiet wood and start
throwing stones around.

Tree Spirit Yes. I lost a twig when his stone hit me.

Crow They need to learn to behave.

Tree Spirit To treat the woods better.

Crow Yes, with some respect.
What was that?

Narrator Hal has thrown another stone,
a smaller one. This time it gets closer
to the crow.

Crow They'll get into trouble
if they behave like that.

Naz Be careful, Hal, you'll get us
into trouble.

Hal Don't be daft. What can happen
to us here?

Naz   Anything could happen.
       We don't know what's here.

Hal   There aren't any dangerous animals
       in these woods.

Naz   What about other things …
       not animals?

Hal   What, like elves and stuff?
       You believe in elves, do you?

Naz   No, of course not.

Hal   Look, see that big pile of stones?
       If anything attacks us
       we can use them.

Narrator Beside the path is a heap of stones,
taller than the two boys.
The stones are piled very neatly.

Naz It looks like someone's put them there.
They're piled up very carefully.

Hal Maybe it was the elves.

Naz Oh, give it a rest, Hal.

Narrator Hal picks up a stone from halfway
up the pile. Underneath is a big,
ugly slug.

Hal Yuck.

Naz It's horrible.

Hal I'll get rid of it.

Narrator Hal picks it up and throws it on the ground. But the slug is really a boggart. It can change its shape to look like anything it wants to.

Boggart Oi. What did I do to you?

Naz That slug said something.

Hal You're going mad.

Boggart You boys need to be careful.

Naz I think we need to be careful.

Hal Not the way I throw.
I can hit anything.
See that crow on the fence over there?
I can knock it off.

Tree Spirit You don't want to do that.

Boggart No. You don't want to do that.

Narrator Hal has not heard them.
He takes aim and throws.
As the stone is about to hit it,
the crow flaps its wings and lifts off
the fence. Then it sits back down
as if nothing has happened.

Tree Spirit You shouldn't have done that.

Boggart There'll be trouble.

Scene 2
Under the spell

Crow   Who threw that?

Narrator The crow knows who did it.
He wants to see if they will admit it.

Hal   A talking crow?
Looks like you're right, Naz.
There *are* weird things in this wood.

(*to the crow*) Anyway, I don't know
who threw a stone at you.
It wasn't us.

Naz   No, it wasn't us.

Boggart You've done it now.

Tree Spirit You've upset the wise old crow.

Narrator All the wood spirits respect the crow.
He is clever and he has magical powers.
It is not a good idea to make
him angry.

Crow You liars. I saw you do it.

Naz Sorry.

Crow You nasty, nose-picking nit breeders.

Hal Now hang on a minute, mate.

Crow I've seen brighter patches of rust
than you two.

Naz Keep your feathers on.
We've said sorry.
We didn't mean to do any damage.

Tree Spirit You broke my twig off.

Boggart You dropped me on the ground.

Tree Spirit Do you know how long it takes
to grow a twig?

Boggart A slug may look ugly
but it still has feelings.

Crow Unlike you two.
You seem to have no feelings at all.

Hal That's not very nice.

Crow Throwing stones isn't very nice.

Naz We didn't mean any harm.

Crow You need to show these woods
a bit more respect. You've hurt a tree
and upset the boggart.

Hal What's a boggart?

Crow You threw him on the ground.

Hal That slug?

Crow   That slug is a boggart.
A spirit that can change to look
like anything it wants to.

Hal   If it can look like anything it wants to,
how come it picks a slug?

Narrator The boggart quickly changes
into a prickly cactus that grows taller
than the boys. The cactus
looks down at them.

Boggart I can look like anything I want to.
Understand?

Crow   You need to learn a lesson.

Hal   We have. I'll never throw a stone
in this wood again – promise.

Naz   I'll make sure he doesn't.
Can we go now please?

Crow   No. You must put right
what you've done wrong.

Hal   Okay.

Naz   How?

Crow   You must find the stone you threw
at me. Then you must put it back
on the cairn – in the same place
that you took it from.

Naz   What's a cairn?

Crow   That big pile of stones is the cairn.

Naz   We won't be able to find that same
stone and put it back in the same
place. It's not possible.

Hal   Forget it. We're going home.
Come on Naz.

Crow   If you don't find that stone
and put it back, your path
will never end.

Hal   What do you mean?

Boggart   The crow always means what he says.

Tree Spirit You will never get to the end
of the path. It will go on for ever.
It will never take you home.

Narrator The crow flies off and sits high up
in an oak tree, looking down
on the boys.

Naz   What are we going to do?

Hal   Go home. No talking crow
is going to scare me.

Tree Spirit You'll never get there.

Boggart   He means what he says.
Unless you find the stone,
the path you take will never end
and you'll never get home.

Naz   This is really creepy.

Hal   Trust me, I know what I'm doing.

Naz   That's what got us into this mess.

Hal   Come on. Let's go home.

Tree Spirit You will be back here again soon.

Boggart   It won't be long before we
see you again.

Crow   See you in a little while.

Narrator The two friends begin to walk quickly
down the path.

Scene 3
Help arrives

Narrator   Naz and Hal hurry along the path
they think will take them home.
But this time, something
feels different.

Naz   It's taking a long time to get out
of the woods today.

Hal   Don't worry. We've been down this
path lots of times before.

Naz   What's that buzzing noise?

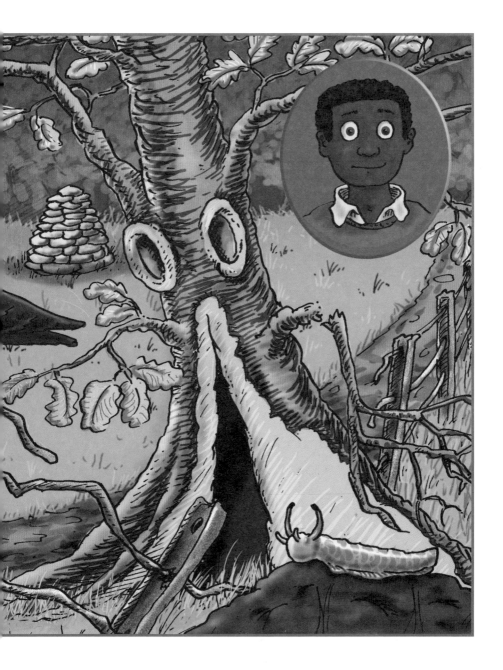

Narrator A very, very big wasp, the size
of a hamster, flies round
the boys' heads.

Hal What the ... ?
I'll throw a stone at it to scare it away.

Naz No, don't.
You'll get us into more trouble.

Boggart No, don't. You could hurt me.

Naz That wasn't a wasp, it was the boggart.

Narrator The wasp buzzes away,
and the boys keep walking.

Hal What's that noise?

Narrator A very loud noise comes from
the bushes. It sounds like
a bear growling.

Naz You said that there weren't
any dangerous animals in the wood.

Hal It'll be the boggart again.

Naz I'm not going to wait and find out.
Come on.

Narrator The boys begin to run along the path.
They run a long way before they stop.

Hal I know this place.

Naz I do too.

Narrator They have come back to where
the trouble started.

Hal This is the place where we met
the crow.

Naz   Yes. We haven't got any closer to home.

Tree Spirit You're back again.
You won't get home until you do
as the crow says.

Narrator They hear the growl again.
Now it is closer and in front of them.

Hal   It's in front of us.

Naz   What can we do?

Narrator The boys stop to think.
A big bear jumps out of a bush.

Hal   Help!

Naz   Get me out of here!

Boggart Boo!

Hal   That's not funny.

Boggart How about this?

Narrator As the boys watch, the boggart changes into a clown.

Naz That's *so* not funny.

Boggart How about this?

Narrator The boggart becomes a bucket of cold custard which begins to tip itself over them.

Tree Spirit How about that?
Do you think that's funny?

Naz That's just disgusting. Stop it.

Boggart I'll stop it when you leave the wood.

Tree Spirit Which will be a long time, if you don't do what the crow says.

Hal But it can't be done.
We can't find that stone in this wood and put it back just where it came from.

Narrator The boggart changes into a bag
of feathers which shakes itself
over the boys. The feathers stick
to the custard.

Hal Ugh – gross! Stop it!

Naz Er … can I ask a question?
Can the boggart turn into
something useful?

Narrator The crow flies past them,
enjoying the fun.

Crow Boggarts can be anything
they want to be.

Boggart What would you like me to be?

Naz A shower.

Crow You have to ask him nicely.

Hal Please, boggart, give us a shower.

Tree Spirit Nicer than that.

Naz   Please Mr Boggart, turn into a shower
and make us clean. We're very sorry
we threw you on the ground.

Hal   Yes. We really are sorry.
And sticky.

Narrator The boggart changes into a hosepipe
and washes all the custard and
feathers off Hal and Naz.

Hal   Thank you, Mr Boggart.

Naz   Yeah, thanks.
Er … you can stop now.

Narrator   The boggart stops spraying the boys.

Hal   Can boggarts ever turn into people?

Crow   They can become anything
they want to be.

Hal   So he could become someone
who can help to solve the problem.

Crow   Maybe, if you ask nicely.

Hal   Mr Boggart, can you please
become someone who can help us to
work out what to do?

Narrator   The boggart changes into
Tommy Tommison, a boy who
is in the same class as Hal and Naz.

Hal   Tommy Tommison! No way!
How are *you* going to be helpful?

Boggart   You think I'm useless.

Hal   No we don't.

Boggart   You always tell me I am.

Naz   Do you know how to find
the stone and put it back?

Boggart   I can't if you think I'm useless.

Naz   We don't think you're useless.

Hal   No, we just tell you you're useless
because we don't like you
being smarter than we are.

Naz   Listen, Tommy – we're sorry
            about all that.

Hal   Yeah, we really need your help.

Crow   This isn't really Tommy, you know.
            It's just the boggart.

Hal   Yeah, I know. But I feel really bad
            about saying all those things to him.

Naz   Me too.

Crow   If you mean it, the boggart
            will help you. If not, what he says
            will make things worse and you will
            never get home.

Narrator   The two boys look at each other
and nod their heads. They mean it.

Hal   Yes. We mean it. We're really sorry
about all the things we've said
to Tommy. We want the boggart
to help us.

Tree Spirit You are beginning to learn
your lesson.

Scene 4
Breaking the spell

Narrator Hal and Naz want to go home.
They are looking for the stone
that Hal threw at the crow.
The boggart is still Tommy Tommison
and he is going to help them –
they hope.

Boggart What did the stone look like?

Hal It was just a stone.
It was the same as all the other stones.

Boggart But no two stones are the same.

Naz It was sort of flat with sharp edges.

Narrator Because boggarts like to play games, the boys are not sure if he is being helpful or not.

Boggart Where did it go when you chucked it?

Hal On the other side of that fence.

Boggart Look at the stones over there.

Naz They're all smooth and round.

Tree Spirit I remember when there was a river there. It was a long time ago.

Hal Why would that make the stones smooth and round?

Naz I don't know. But we did this at school. I bet Tommy Tommison knows.

Narrator   The boys turn to look at the boggart.
He does look like Tommy, but can
they trust him? And why should
Tommy help them anyway?
They haven't exactly been best mates
to him.

Boggart   Stones at the bottom of rivers
are made smooth by the water
running over them.

Naz   I think he's right.

Hal   Me too. But how does that help?

Naz   We'll know which stone is the one
you threw because it will be
the only one that's flat
with sharp edges.
Let's look over there.

Tree Spirit Be careful when you look
in the bushes. Don't do any more
damage.

Hal   Okay, okay!
We'll be careful.

Naz   You look over there.
I'll look over here.

Narrator The two friends begin to search
the floor of the wood, looking
for a flat stone among the round ones.

Hal   Got one.

Naz   Let's see.

Tree Spirit Is it flat?

Hal   Yes.

Boggart Has it got sharp edges?

Naz   Yes.

Crow   That was the easy part.
Now you have to put it back
on the cairn just where
you took it from.

Narrator Hal carries the stone towards
the cairn.

Hal How will we find the place
we took it from?

Naz It doesn't look like there's
a stone missing from it.

Crow What a pity. You will have to stay
in the woods for ever.
You will never get home.

Hal I picked up the stone from here.

Naz There was a slug underneath.

Tree Spirit Are you sure it was a slug?

Hal   Yeah … er, no.
It was the boggart, wasn't it?

Naz   Mr Boggart, now we've found the stone
we don't need you to be
Tommy Tommison any more.

Hal   No. Please would you become
a slug again and show us where
you were lying?

Boggart All right. But you won't throw me
on the ground again, will you?

Hal   Believe me – if I ever get out
of this wood, I'm never going to throw
anything anywhere, ever again.

Naz   Me neither.

Boggart Okay. I'll try and remember
which stone I was lying on.

Narrator The boggart changes into a slug.
He slowly crawls up the pile of stones
until he gets to where he was lying
before.

Boggart This is it.

Hal So if we put this stone on top of you
now, it will be in the right place.

Naz I hope he's telling the truth.
If not, we'll never get home.

Hal Let's try it.

Narrator Hal puts the stone on top of the slug.

Hal Nothing's happened.

Naz Is the spell broken?
Can we go home?

Narrator The big, black crow lands on the fence, just where it was before.

Crow Have you put the stone back
in just the same place you took it from?

Hal I think so.

Crow What have you learnt?

Hal To respect the woods.

Crow Anything else?

Naz That we shouldn't pick on people
like Tommy just because they're clever.

Crow Anything else?

Hal Never to throw stones at crows.

Crow   That one is very important.
             The spell is lifted.
             The path will take you home.

Hal   Thank you, Crow.
             We won't bother you again.

Naz   No, you've seen the last of us.

Tree Spirit You are always welcome to visit
             the woods. But you must always
             treat them with respect.

Narrator But the boys don't hear him.
             They are already running off
             along the path. And they won't
             be back any time soon.

45

Drama ideas

After Scene 1

- Hotseating: Choose one person to be Naz.
- Everyone else can ask Naz questions, e.g. how does he feel about the woods? Is he more scared than he's letting on to Hal?

After Scene 2

- With a partner, pretend to be the crow and the boggart.
- What do they think of Naz and Hal? How might they plan to get their own back on the boys? Act out a short discussion between them.

3

After Scene 3

- In your group, each choose a character from the play. Imagine the character's thoughts at the end of the scene.

- Take on the role of your character, and tell the rest of the group what you are thinking.

After Scene 4

- With a partner, imagine a conversation between the boys as they run home.

- How do they feel about what happened in the woods? Are they looking forward to getting home? Act out a short discussion between them.

4

PHONE
0871 47 23 010

www.risingstars-uk.com